Scholastic Literacy Skills

CW00328230

VOCABULARY

Term-by-Term Photocopiables

AUTHORS CLAIRE COLLING, VAL GREEN,
CHRIS HOLLOWAY AND SALLY JOHNSON
EDITOR KATE PEARCE
ASSISTANT EDITOR ROANNE DAVIS
SERIES DESIGNER MARK UDALL
DESIGNER PAUL CHESHIRE
ILLUSTRATIONS RAY AND CORINNE BURROWS
Designed using Adobe Pagemaker
Published by Scholastic Ltd, Villiers House, Clarendon
Avenue, Leamington Spa, Warwickshire CV32 5PR
Text © Claire Colling, Val Green,
Chris Holloway and Sally Johnson
© 2000 Scholastic Ltd
2 3 4 5 6 7 8 9 0   1 2 3 4 5 6 7 8
British Library Cataloguing-in-Publication Data
A catalogue record for this book is available
from the British Library.
ISBN 0-439-01640-1

Contents

Vocabulary

The four books in this series are designed to develop children's vocabulary skills through progressive worksheets that are structured to fit the school year.

Written by practising teachers, the content emphasizes the development of vocabulary and spelling based on the word and sentence level requirements of the National Literacy Strategy *Framework for Teaching*.

The photocopiable worksheets in each book give opportunities for pupils to work independently of the teacher to enhance their word power. Alternatively, teachers may wish to use the sheets as a focus for whole-class shared teaching or for homework.

Themes

Each Vocabulary book is loosely arranged on a theme of 'exploration'. This reinforces the idea that children, by exploring and being curious about words, will develop strategies for further increasing their word power. The themes for each book are:

- ❏ ages 7–8: Jungle explorer
- ❏ ages 8–9: Underwater explorer
- ❏ ages 9–10: Underground explorer
- ❏ ages 10–11: Space explorer

Word Explorer

Each Vocabulary book contains a photocopiable Word Explorer booklet which matches the theme of the book. The Word Explorer encourages each child to collect new words and learn new meanings by building a personal wordbank. On some worksheets, it is suggested that the children write down new words in their Word Explorer, as indicated by the magnifying glass symbol. In addition, teachers may choose themes or sets of words related to a topic or particular theme being covered by the class at the time, for example words related to a topic on the Greeks, or a science theme such as 'photosynthesis', could be collected.

Treasure Tests

The Treasure Test words are target words that children should learn. There are six pages of these in each book, two for each term, which children can take home to learn (see pages 9, 10, 26, 27, 45 and 46). They can test their knowledge of Treasure Test words at the end of each term with the Treasure Chest sheet on page 64. Teachers may choose to use this as an assessment guide in the form of a test or, alternatively, children of similar ability could test each other to reinforce their knowledge.

The Treasure Tests are progressive and consolidatory – that is, the word lists for ages 8–9 revise and consolidate vocabulary from the ages 7–8 Vocabulary book, and so on. The children may wish to keep the Treasure Test sheets and Word Explorer booklets in their own personal folders or portfolios.

Answers

These are given on pages 4–6. Some activities are open-ended and, where appropriate, suggestions are provided.

Guide to symbols used

 = magnifying glass. This denotes new or challenging words which should be added to the Word Explorer booklet.

 = dictionary/thesaurus. This symbol indicates children will need to use a dictionary and/or thesaurus to complete the task.

 = Treasure Chest. The Treasure Chest symbol denotes more challenging tasks which may be suitable for extension work.

Answers

Thoughts of home (page 11)

mother; father; brother; sister.

Tom's diary (page 12)

Passage order: midnight; light; sight; fright; tight; might; plight; bright; night; delight.

The sea (page 13)

In order: run; shore; land; hand; grey; deep; bones; light; sun.

Sounds familiar (1) (page 14)

1. two 2. tide 3. sails 4. rows 5. their 6. blue 7. sea
8. pier.

Sounds familiar (2) (page 15)

1. buoy, by 2. course 3. current 4. quay 5. crews
6. cruise 7. missed, mist 8. mussels.
The sentence should be similar to: Homophones are words that sound exactly the same but have different meanings and spellings.

Down to the roots (page 16)

invent; describe; danger; beauty; marry; anger; colour; illustrate.
Answers could include: appearance, appearing, disappear, appeared; destroyed, destroying, destructive; liked, liking, likeable, alike; agreed, agreeable, agreement, disagreement; circled, encircled, circling, circular; helped, helpful, unhelpful; built, building, rebuild; playful, playing, played.

Past, present, future (page 17)

1. falling 2. went 3. will write 4. ran 5. swam
6. will ride 7. enjoy 8. tell 9. heard 10. was.
Present tense (red): is falling, enjoy, tell. Past tense (black): went, ran, swam, heard, was. Future tense (blue): will write, will ride.

Regular and irregular (page 18)

Regular: hope/hoped; pick/picked; laugh/laughed; kick/kicked; walk/walked; love/loved; climb/climbed.
Irregular: lose/lost; fight/fought; know/knew; give/gave; catch/caught; am/was; sit/sat; light/lit; sing/sang; can/could; speak/spoke; tell/told.

Select a suffix (1) (page 19)

In any order: leadership; atomic; original; hardship; stationary; national; heroic; missionary.

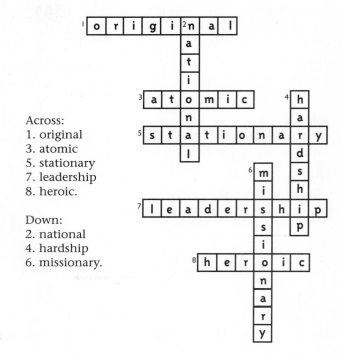

Across:
1. original
3. atomic
5. stationary
7. leadership
8. heroic.

Down:
2. national
4. hardship
6. missionary.

Select a suffix (2) (page 20)

usefulness; treatment; knighthood; greatness; childhood; improvement.

Across:
3. improvement.

Down:
1. childhood
2. greatness.

Say that again! (page 21)

The answers should be similar to: Raining very hard. Getting up early and going to bed late, not getting much sleep, being very active.
Having 40 winks: having a quick nap.
Let the cat out of the bag: to tell a secret.

Get in order (page 22)

In order: shark, shell, ship, shore, shrimp, shy.
In order: shade, shake, shallow, shampoo, shark, shave.

Fishy fun (page 23)

In any order: comment; muddle; lorry/lolly; bossy; hammer/hatter; follow; happy; hammock/haddock; bubble; bottle; runny.

Treasure hunt (page 24)

hunt – hunting; fear – afraid/frightened; food – feed; thirst– thirsty; sight – saw; delight – delighted; knowledge – know; song – sang; growth – grew; discovery – discovered; threat – threatened; leave – left; death – die.

Adverbs underwater (page 25)

Some adjectives are interchangeable, but a suggested order is given here: quickly/swiftly; swiftly/quickly; gracefully/gently; gently/gracefully; sometimes; menacingly; above; gently/slowly; peacefully; Here; silently; soon; fiercely.

Ahoy! (page 28)

1. floating 2. on the shore 3. in the air.
1. atop 2. amend 3. away 4. afresh.
almost; already; altogether; always.
Answer similar to: The second l is deleted.

Pearl fishers (page 29)

Liked – enjoyed; asked – begged; went – sailed; get – collect; said no – refused; said – insisted; sure – certain; get – retrieve; make – build; nice – lovely or wonderful; good – wonderful or lovely; see – notice; little way – short distance; went – dived; big – huge or massive; go – pass; group – shoal; swam quickly – darted; came up – surfaced; big – huge or massive; came home – returned; happy – delighted; biggest – largest; worth a lot of money – valuable.

Find the partners (page 30)

prince – princess; heiress – heir; god – goddess; steward – stewardess; duke – duchess; lioness – lion; waiter – waitress; king – queen; tigress – tiger; hostess – host; bride – groom.

Take your partners! (page 31)

Chicken: cock – hen; Horse: stallion – mare; Cattle: bull – cow; Rabbit: buck – doe; Sheep: ram – ewe; Pig: boar – sow; Goat: billy – nanny.

New for old (page 32)

frock = dress; wireless = radio; looking glass = mirror; charabanc = coach; perambulator = pram; counterpane = bedspread.

Willing and able (page 33)

1. washable 2. agreeable 3. enjoyable 4. usable 5. breakable 6. pliable 7. readable 8. reliable.

Safe and sound (page 34)

Answers should be similar to: legible – able to be read; reversible – able to be reversed; possible – able to be done; incredible – hardly able to be believed; invisible – not able to be seen; responsible – able to look after; sensible – able to use sense; flexible – able to be bent; visible – able to be seen; edible – able to be eaten.

Adding to adjectives (page 35)

hot, hotter, hottest; hungry, hungrier, hungriest; cold, colder, coldest.
1. sillier, silliest 2. bluer, bluest 3. narrower, narrowest.

Similar shells (page 36)

extremely hot; quite cold; Jasjeet; Tom; Stephen.

Find my mate (page 37)

In any order: they have – they've; it is – it's; do not – don't; we have – we've; he is – he's; were not – weren't; they are – they're.

Long and short (page 38)

had not; does not; have not; has not; were not; could not; was not.
In order: can't; haven't; didn't; it's; hasn't; wouldn't; don't; haven't; I'll.

Underwater apostrophes (1) (page 39)

The diver's helmet; The crab's claw; The dolphin's fin; The seahorse's eye/head; The lobster's leg/claw; The mermaid's tail; Nessie's neck; The shark's mouth/jaw/teeth.

Underwater apostrophes (2) (page 40)

The divers' helmets; The crabs' claws; The dolphins' fins; The seahorses' heads/eyes; The lobsters' legs/claws; The mermaids' tails; The sea-monsters' necks; The sharks' mouths/teeth/jaws.

Columbus claims possession (page 41)

Contractions (red): weren't; They'd; didn't; wasn't; they'd; they'd; He'd.
Possessive words (blue): Columbus's; Maria's; sailor's; captain's; Salvador's.

Make the join (page 42)

1. but, as. 2. because, however. 3.until, so.

What shall we do with the drunken sailor? (page 43)

1. Get on your knees and scrub the decks. 2. When we reach the next island we'll bury our treasure. 3. Get the broom and sweep my cabin. It is very untidy. 4. Get below and cook my breakfast! 5. The ship has struck a rock! Help! We're sinking.
Children's own explanations.

As good as gold (page 46)

Suggested answers are as follows, although the children make invent others that also make sense:
1. button/new pin 2. ice 3. cucumber 4. pancake 5. daisy 6. grass 7. nails 8. fire 9. feather 10. fox/flash.

Words, words and more words (page 47)

Words beginning with v (in any order): video, very, van, vet, voice, vowel, visit, vampire. Words with v in the middle (in any order): level, solve, brave, live, sleeve, river, having, move. Words beginning with v and also having v in the middle: (written at the bottom of the letter V): valve, velvet.
Top row: a as in day. Bottom row: a as in hat.

Spelling rule: answers may vary.
word, work, world, worm, worst, worship. Or is
pronounced like er.

Walrus words (page 48)

1. work 2. woman 3. wall 4. wolf 5. walrus
6. wonder/wander 7. water 8. warn/worn 9. word/
ward 10. world 11. worship 12. won.

Sound it out! (page 49)

tough: enough, rough; thought: fought, bought;
plough: slough, bough; could: should, would; hour:
flour, sour; pour: four, tour.
Suggestions: bright: light, fright,
sight; judge: fudge, budge, trudge.

Porthole problems (page 50)

1. unlocked, unhappy
2. disappearing, exit 3. non-fiction,
exported 4. decode, disagreed
5. prevented, re-entered 6. (in any
order) antiseptics, antibiotics
7. misfortune, mistake 8. decreased
9. recaptured 10. co-operates.

What a catch! (page 51)

In any order: -ible: visible; possible;
horrible; responsible; terrible.
-ive: attractive; relative; massive;
adjective; active.
-tion: direction; subtraction;
exploration; imagination; education.
-able: valuable; washable; remarkable; fashionable;
enjoyable.
-sion: decision; permission; explosion; television;
admission.

Captain Stone's tattoos (page 52)

In any order: -ist: scientist; pianist; motorist; cyclist.
-tion: relation; addition; subtraction; attraction.
-ive: attractive; reflective; supportive; active; secretive.
-ful: beautiful; colourful; wonderful; harmful.
-ly: sadly; happily; calmly; gladly.
(Other answers are also possible, eg additive; action;
secretly; attractive; reflection; relative.)

It's and Its (page 53)

2. It's 3. It's 4. its 5. Its 6. It's 7. its 8. its 9. its 10.
it's 11. it's 12. it's.

Gone fishing (page 54)

some+thing; hand+bag; cup+board; after+noon;
tooth+ache; home+work; thunder+storm; sauce+pan.

Animal diminutives (page 55)

cow – calf; cat – kitten; horse – foal; hare – leveret;
frog – tadpole; eel – elver; swan – cygnet; goose –
gosling; fox – cub; lion – cub; sheep – lamb.

More diminutives (page 56)

book; house; duck; owl; hill; pig; goose; kitchen; tree.
The suffixes used are -let; -ling; -ette; -ock.
Odd ones out: 'sapling' – small tree; maisonette (all
the others are built on the root word.)
Maisonette from 'maison' – French for house.

Argue the point! (page 57)

1. unless 2. because 3. if 4. so 5. then.

Can you ask a question? (page 58)

Are there many exciting creatures that live in the sea?
Is it necessary to wear a life jacket when you go
sailing? Can you often find crabs in rock pools on the
beach? Is it fun to make sandcastles on the beach?

Test your tenses! (page 59)

I showed; I wanted; I wished; I waited; I picked; I
played; I looked; I touched; I
asked.
I tried; I spied; I married; I
hurried; I buried.
I hummed; I patted; I begged; I
tripped; I trotted.
(a)   Change 'y' to 'i' and add
'ed'.
(b) Double final consonant and
add 'ed'.
2. John will travel home by bus.
3. They will love their presents.
4. She will place the books on
the shelf 5. Mum will drive to
work.

Treasures of the sea (page 60)

In order: was; swam; could;
were; darted; disappeared; felt; passed; plunged;
helped; was; were; glistened; sparkled; caught;
swayed; swirled; lay; was.

Danger at sea! (page 61)

In order: sails; flap; have; head; becomes; are; feel;
grow; rocks; see; has; cannot; can; notice; swimming;
gulp; is; can; shudder; breathe; realize; has; is; leaps;
heads; seems; am; appears; grab; turn; leads.

Get it right (page 62)

1. There is more sea than land. 2. The largest seas are
called oceans. 3. Oceans are as deep as mountains are
high. 4. The Atlantic Ocean is about five thousand
kilometres across. 5. Some of the first Atlantic
explorers were the Vikings. 6. They crossed the ocean
and discovered America. 7. This was five hundred
years before Columbus set out. 8. Vikings travelled in
long ships which had large sails. 9. On the front of
the ship was a carving of a dragon's head. 10. If there
was no wind oars were used to propel the long ship.

How well can you spell? (page 63)

yung – young; bother – brother; muver – mother;
farther – father; didunt – didn't; leve – leave; evry –
every; thort – thought; brithday – birthday; mornin –
morning; opend – opened; jumpt – jumped; chanje –
change; muny – money; new – knew; mite – might;
nevver – never; walkt – walked; fownd – found; a
cross – across; befor – before; begane – began; thinck –
think; werk – work; oan – own; leve – leave; thort –
thought; betta – better; secund – second; rite – right;
plaice – place; wite – white; tolled – told; happie –
happy; stoped – stopped; togeather – together; mutch

Word Explorer

Year: _____

Name _____

Class _____

Suggested colour key (guide):

Diver: black
Shells: pink
Ocean: shades of blue/
green/purple

Octopus: grey
Fish: multicoloured
Seaweed: shades of green/yellow
Stones and pebbles: brown

Home address

_____

_____

_____

School address

_____

_____

_____

❏ Write any new words you have learned.

Treasure Test 1

❏ Can you spell these words on your empty Treasure Chest sheet? Ask a friend to test you on them. Remember! Look, say, cover, write, check. Write each word three times. Every time you get it right, colour in a pearl in the Treasure Chest shell.

ask · asked · began · being

brought · can't · change · coming

didn't · does · done · don't

face · fair · fast · found

goes · gone · heard · I'm

join · jumped · knew · know

leave · lend · less · letter

❏ Write the ones you find tricky in your Word Explorer.

vocabulary

VOCABULARY

photocopiable

Treasure Test 2

❑ Can you spell these words on your empty Treasure Chest sheet? Ask a friend to test you on them. Remember! Look, say, cover, write, check. Write each word three times. Every time you get it right, colour in a pearl in the Treasure Chest shell.

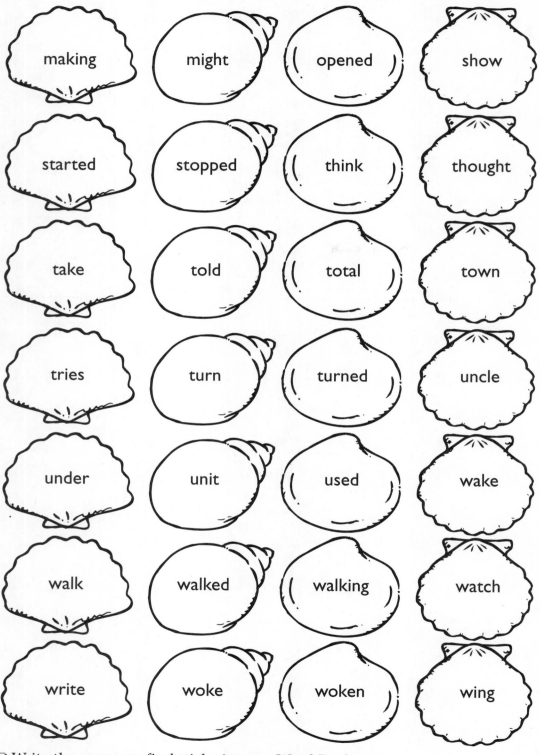

❑ Write the ones you find tricky in your Word Explorer.

Thoughts of home

moth_ _

fath_ _

sist_ _

me!

broth_ _

❏ Add the correct phoneme to the picture above.

❏ Now draw and label your own family:

Tom's diary

❏ Add the phoneme **–ight** to the letters shown around the candle.
Write the new words in your Word Explorer.

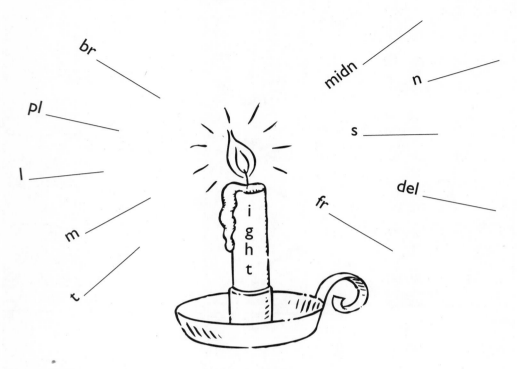

br _____

midn _____   n _____

pl _____

s _____

l _____

del _____

m _____

fr _____

t _____

i
g
h
t

❏ Use the words you have made to complete Tom the cabin boy's diary:

Saturday 3rd September 1750

It was _____ when I saw by the _____

of my candle a _____ which made me tremble with

_____. My throat felt _____ when I tried to

cry out with all my _____. I was alone and aware of

my _____. A _____ sword was gleaming in

the _____. It was held by a shadowy figure. As he

spoke, to my _____ I realized it was my friend,

Captain Benbow.

The sea

❏ Find the correct rhyming words in the stones to fill the spaces in the poem:

So still the sea lies sleeping,
Beneath the sparkling sun,
While rivers on their journeys
To wider oceans _____.

Quietly now the waves creep o'er
The pebbles on the shingle _____
And soothe the sand,
And stroke the _____
With gentle touch of watery _____.

Fiercely now the breakers come,
Lashing the shore with mighty roar,
In furious spray
Of green and _____,
Spilling the foam in bright array.

Then calm again the oceans sleep,
A mystic world there in the _____
Of tangled weed and polished stones,
Of wrecks and decks and long lost _____,
Of dark and dismal shapes in endless night
And then of shoals of fish in wondrous _____.

And does the sea lie sleeping,
Beneath the sparkling _____,
While rivers on their journeys
To wider oceans run?

C. Holloway

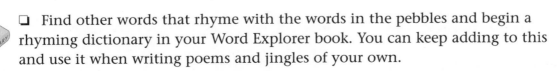

land
grey
deep
bones
shore
sun
hand
run
light

❏ Find other words that rhyme with the words in the pebbles and begin a rhyming dictionary in your Word Explorer book. You can keep adding to this and use it when writing poems and jingles of your own.

Sounds familiar (1)

❑ Choose the correct homophone to complete each sentence.
Then check in a dictionary to make sure you have chosen the right one.

1 There are _____ ships out at sea.
(two, too or to?)

2 The ships had to wait for high _____ before they could leave port.
(tied or tide?)

3 The ship's _____ billowed in the strong wind.
(sales or sails?)

4 There were _____ of portholes along the sides of the ships.
(rose or rows?)

5 The ships dropped _____ anchors in the shelter of the bay.
(their or there?)

6 The sky was a brilliant _____ after the storm had cleared.
(blue or blew?)

7 The ships couldn't set off because there was a storm at _____.
(see or sea?)

8 A boy was fishing from the end of the _____.
(peer or pier?)

reel and real

❑ Now write two sentences of your own, one including **reel** and the other including **real**. Show that you understand the meanings of each of these words.

1 _____

_____

_____

2 _____

_____

_____

Sounds familiar (2)

❑ Choose the correct homophone to complete each sentence.
Then check in a dictionary to make sure you have chosen the right one.

1 The _____ bobbed up and down as the ship glided
   _____.
   (buoy or boy, by or buy?)

2 The _____ of the ship took it away from the dangerous rocks.
   (coarse or course?)

3 The strong _____ swept the raft across the sea.
   (currant or current?)

4 The ship headed for the _____.
   (key or quay?)

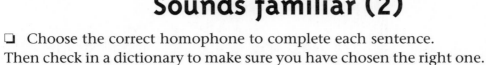

5 The ships' _____ waved to one another.
   (crews or cruise?)

6 The holidaymakers were going on a Mediterranean _____.
   (crews or cruise?)

7 Fortunately, the two ships _____ one another as they sailed
   blindly through the _____.
   (mist or missed?)

8 The sailors ate _____ for their dinners.
   (mussels or muscles?)

Here are five key words:

   spelling   sound   different   same   meaning

❑ Can you use all these words in a sentence to explain what homophones are?

_____

_____

_____

_____

Down to the roots

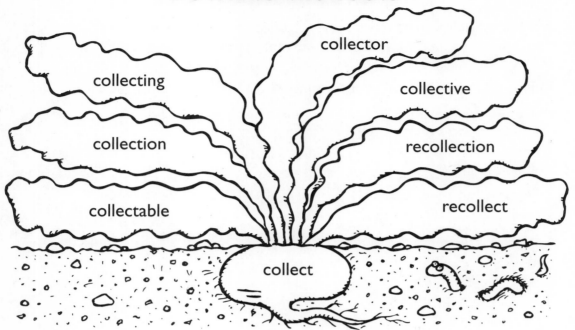

The illustration above shows a number of words that have the root word **collect** in them, for example <u>collect</u>ing, <u>collect</u>ion, re<u>collect</u>.

❑ Write down the root word from which each of these words grew. Use your dictionary if you need help, but try to think of the answers yourself first.

For example:

| explosion ⟶ explode | loving ⟶ love |

inventive _____   marriage _____

description _____   angry _____

dangerous _____   colourful _____

beautiful _____   illustration _____

❑ Now think of longer words which grew from these root words:

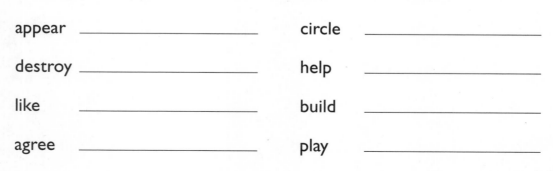

appear _____   circle _____

destroy _____   help _____

like _____   build _____

agree _____   play _____

Past, present and future

A verb is an action word. It tells... what is being done (present)
or what has been done (past)
or what is going to be done (future).

Present, past and future are verb **tenses**.

❑ Choose the correct verb from the bracket to fit each space in the sentences:

1 The rain is _____ heavily.
(falling, fell, will fall)

2 Last night I _____ to bed late.
(go, went, will go)

3 Tomorrow I _____ to my penfriend.
(write, wrote, will write)

4 She _____ as fast as she could.
(is running, ran, will run)

5 Robert _____ well and won his race.
(swims, swam, will swim)

6 I _____ my new bicycle next week.
(ride, rode, will ride)

7 Do you _____ reading poetry?
(enjoy, enjoyed, will enjoy)

8 Please _____ me another story!
(tell, told, will tell)

9 Yesterday Theo _____ a strange noise during the night.
(hears, heard, will hear)

10 When I was a child, my favourite hobby _____ ice-skating.
(is, was, will be)

❑ Now circle the verbs you have written in these colours:
red — present tense
black — past tense
blue — future tense

Regular and irregular

Some verbs are regular verbs. This means –**ed** is added to the root word to change it to the past tense.

| I play (present) | $\longrightarrow$ | I played (past) |

I play (present) $\longrightarrow$ I played (past)

She jumps (present) $\longrightarrow$ She jumped (past)

Some verbs are irregular verbs. This means that the words used to show past and present are quite different:

I go (present) $\longrightarrow$ I went (past)

He sees (present) $\longrightarrow$ He saw (past)

❑ Look at these pairs of verbs (present and past) and decide whether the verbs are regular or irregular. Write the pairs in the correct column. Two have been done for you.

lose/lost   hope/hoped   can/could   love/loved

wish/wished   pick/picked   speak/spoke   climb/climbed

fight/fought   laugh/laughed   walk/walked   tell/told

know/knew

give/gave   sit/sat

catch/caught   light/lit

am/was   sing/sang

break/broke   kick/kicked

Irregular verbs

break/broke

Regular verbs

wish/wished

Select a suffix (1)

A suffix is a morpheme that is added to the end of a word to change its meaning. It can have one or more syllables.

❑ Add the correct suffix from the list shown on the octopus – **ship**, **al**, **ic**, **ary** – to each of the octopus's tentacles. You will need to use each suffix twice.

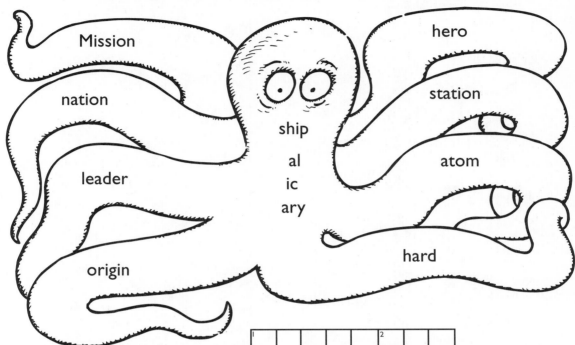

❑ Now match each word to its dictionary definition to complete the crossword:

Across
1 Earliest or first
3 To do with atom bombs
5 Not moving
7 To be in charge of something you must be good at this
8 To do something very brave would be this

Down
2 Belonging to a nation
4 Suffering
6 A person who travels and teaches about their religion

Select a suffix (2)

A suffix has one or more syllables and comes at the end of a word.

❑ Draw a line to link each pearl with the correct shell.

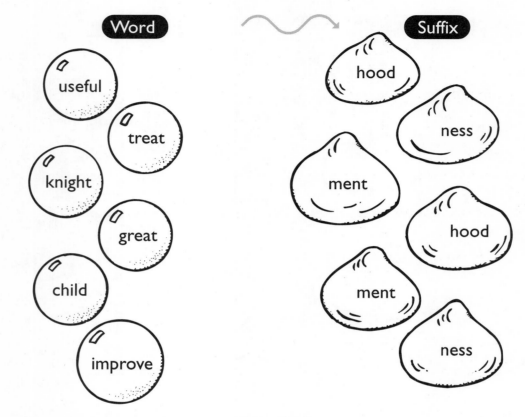

❑ Now complete this puzzle using three of the new words:

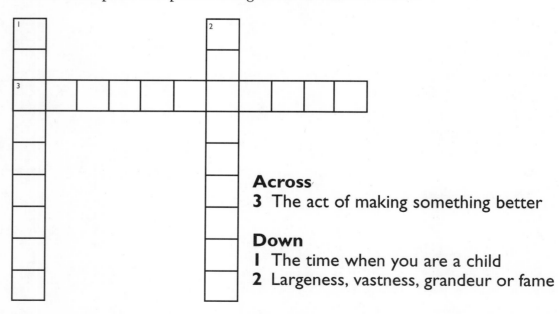

Across
3 The act of making something better

Down
1 The time when you are a child
2 Largeness, vastness, grandeur or fame

 ❑ Make up a word puzzle of your own using the three words that are left. You can use a dictionary to help you make up the clues. See if your friend can solve it!

Say that again!

Sometimes we use idioms in our speech. Idioms are sayings that mean something different from the actual words that have been used. For example, when we say someone is 'as sick as a parrot' what we really mean is that they are very unhappy. Here are some more idioms:

Getting into hot water

Literal meaning: being in hot water.
Idiomatic meaning: getting into trouble.

Sent to Coventry

Literal meaning: being told to travel to Coventry
Idiomatic meaning: being ignored as a punishment

❏ What are the idiomatic meanings of these sayings?

Raining cats and dogs

_____

_____

_____

Burning the candle at both ends

_____

_____

_____

❏ Now think of the idiom – the saying – that matches these literal meanings:

Bat your eyelids 40 times

Idiom: _____

_____

Idiomatic meaning: _____

_____

Allow the cat to escape from the bag

Idiom: _____

_____

Idiomatic meaning: _____

_____

❏ How many idioms do you know? More than you might think! Test your friends – write down the meanings, and see if they can work out the idiom!

Get in order

a b c d e f g h i j k l m n o p q r s t u v w x y z

When words are listed in alphabetical order, for example in a dictionary, and the first two letters of the words are the same, they are then put in order according to the **third** letters. For example:

ha<u>b</u>it   ha<u>d</u>   hai<u>r</u>   hal<u>f</u>   ha<u>mm</u>er   ha<u>n</u>dle

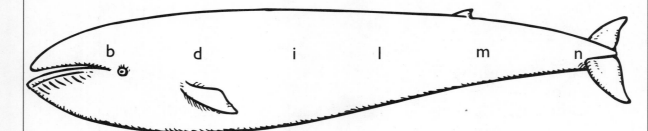

b, d, i, l, m and **n** are in alphabetical order.
❏ Underline the third letter in each of these words, and then arrange the words alphabetically in the whale:

shrimp   shell   shy   shark   ship   shore

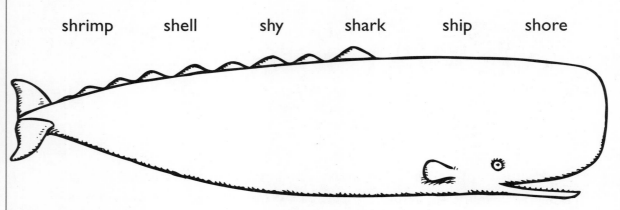

When the first three letters of words are the same, the words are alphabetically ordered according to the **fourth** letters. Underline the fourth letter in each of these words, and then put the words in alphabetical order in the whale:

shampoo   shave   shake   shark   shade   shallow

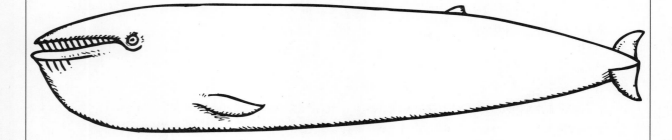

Fishy fun

Some words have a double consonant. This is where a word has two consonant letters next to each other, such as:

bu<u>bb</u>le   ke<u>tt</u>le   com<u>m</u>on

❑ Write the missing double consonant for each word in the fish. Use the sea-bed at the bottom of the page to help you.

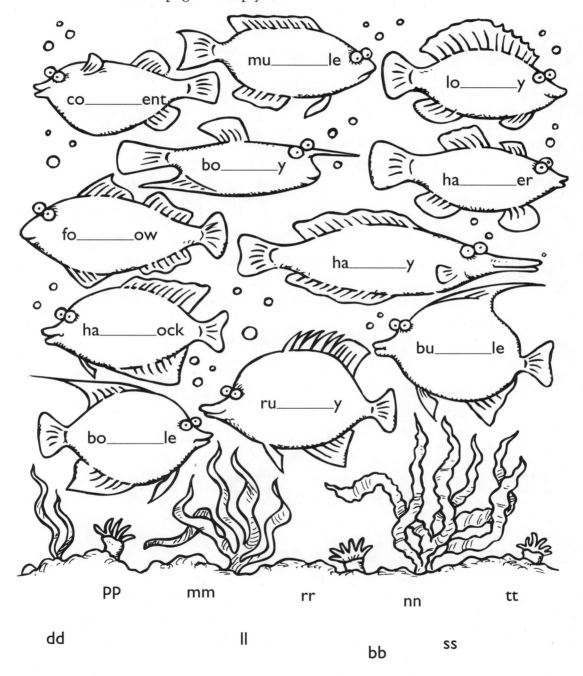

PP   mm   rr   nn   tt

dd   ll   bb   ss

❑ Now look for some other words in your dictionary that have double consonants.

Treasure hunt

Some of the verbs in this tale are missing. Above each space is the word that is missing, but in the form of a noun.

❏ Change these words into verbs and insert them into the story so it makes sense. Read it carefully to make sure you have changed the words correctly. The first one has been done for you.

Captain Stone, you're all alone!

Captain Stone and his band of pirates were [hunt] _hunting_ for buried

treasure.

They had been at sea for many weeks. They were [fear] _____ that

sharks would [food] _____ on them if they fell overboard. They had

no clean water to drink and were very [thirst] _____. Finally, they

[sight] _____ an island in the distance. The crew were [delight] _____

to have reached land once more – and so was Captain Stone!

"I [knowledge] _____ where treasure is buried on this island," growled

the Captain.

He led his men to a palm tree. They [song] _____ merrily as they

dug into the soft sand, watched carefully by the Captain. They [growth] _____

very excited as they [discovery] _____ a chest. They would

all be rich! But, suddenly, the Captain drew his sword and

[threat] _____ to kill his favourite crew. He wanted all the treasure for

himself, to sell when they returned home! Quick as a flash, the crew fled

back to the ship, set sail once more and [leave] _____ the Captain

there to [death] _____, alone except for his useless treasure.

Adverbs underwater

An adverb tells us how, when or where the action of a verb takes place.
For example:

He ran **quickly**   (the adverb tells us **how** he ran)
Come back **soon** (the adverb tells us **when**)
Put it **there**   (the adverb tells us **where**)

Many adverbs end in **–ly**, but not all.

❏ Using the adverbs in the picture below, fill in the gaps in the passage.
You can only use each adverb in the picture once.

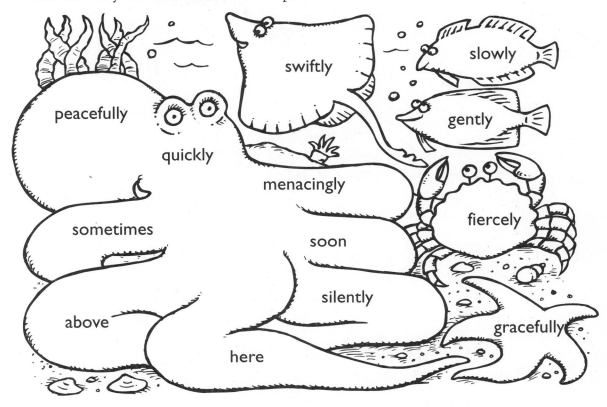

A huge octopus crawls _____ over the rocks of the sea-bed,

hunting for crabs which scuttle _____ away into the sand. Shoals

of brightly-coloured fish dart _____ among the seaweed, which

sways _____ in the ocean current. _____ the shadow

of a shark looms _____ _____. Starfish float

_____ past the wreck of a sunken ship which lies

_____ on the ocean floor. _____ is a place where long-

lost treasures and ancient bones lie, _____ keeping their secrets.

_____ darkness will descend upon the restless waters and

monstrous waves will crash _____ on the surface of the deep.

Treasure Test 1

❏ Can you spell these words on your empty Treasure Chest sheet? Ask a friend to test you on them. Remember! Look, say, cover, write, check. Write each word three times. Every time you get it right, colour in a pearl in the Treasure Chest shell.

almost	along	always	any
before	being	better	blow
calm	card	case	cash
during	every	finger	first
half	hide	hold	hope
morning	much	never	night
nod	noon	north	now

❏ Write the ones you find tricky in your Word Explorer.

Treasure Test 2

❏ Can you spell these words on your empty Treasure Chest sheet? Ask a friend to test you on them. Remember! Look, say, cover, write, check. Write each word three times. Every time you get it right, colour in a pearl in the Treasure Chest shell.

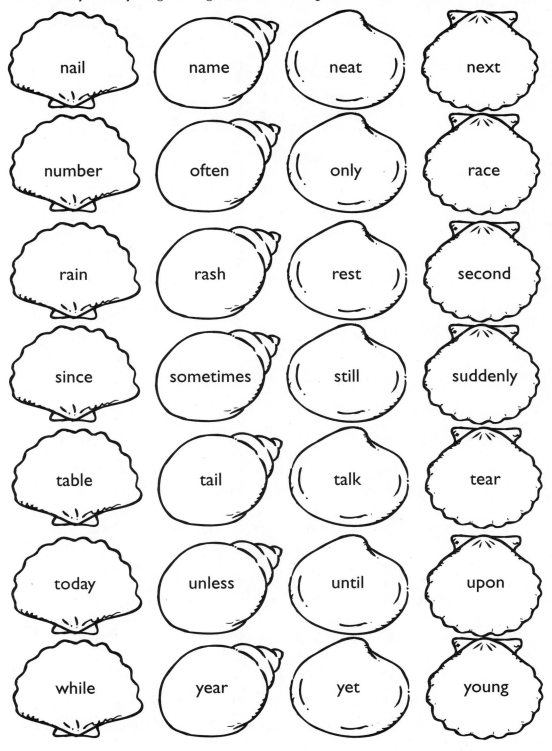

nail	name	neat	next
number	often	only	race
rain	rash	rest	second
since	sometimes	still	suddenly
table	tail	talk	tear
today	unless	until	upon
while	year	yet	young

❏ Write the ones you find tricky in your Word Explorer.

Ahoy!

Do you know that the letter **a** can be a prefix?
When it is used as a prefix it can mean **on**, **to**, **in** or **in the process of**.

The raft is **afloat**.

The man is **ashore**.

The flag is **aloft**.

❏ In your own words write in the meanings of:

1 afloat _____

2 ashore _____

3 aloft _____

                                             ❏ Check in your dictionary.

❏ Now see if you can match each of these words beginning with the prefix **a** to its correct definition:

1 on the summit: _____

2 making something correct: _____   amend

3 in the process of leaving: going _____   away   afresh

4 to start something again: to start _____   atop

❏ Read this passage.

> The shipwrecked sailor had almost finished preparing for his
> escape from the island. He had already filled a barrel of water and
> had placed it and the fruit he had collected altogether on the raft.
> Since he had been on the island, he had always tied the raft to the
> palm tree so that it wouldn't float away. But this time he had
> forgotten, and now it had all gone!

❏ Underline the words in the passage that contain the prefix **al**. Write them in your Word Explorer.
How does the spelling of **all** change when it becomes a prefix? _____

Pearl fishers

A story can often be improved by the use of more interesting words, especially to replace overused words such as **got**, **nice**, **good**, **went**, **big** and **said**.

❑ Replace the underlined words with more interesting ones from the pearls. Make sure that the meaning is the same. Join them with dotted lines.

dived

retrieve

notice

collect

insisted

build

sailed

short distance

returned

pass

delighted

shoal

The pearl diver

When I was at school I <u>liked</u> singing a song called 'Quinoro's Pearl'. It was a song about a boy who wanted to be a pearl diver. Quinoro <u>asked</u> the fishermen to take him with them when they <u>went</u> out to sea to <u>get</u> oysters. But the fishermen <u>said no</u>. He was too young, they <u>said</u>. It was too dangerous for such a young boy. Quinoro might be attacked by sharks, or drown in the deep, blue sea.

Quinoro was sad. He was <u>sure</u> he could <u>get</u> pearls from the sea bed, so he decided to <u>make</u> a raft of his own. One <u>nice</u> sunny day he set sail, secretly following the fishermen. It was a <u>good</u> day for diving.

The pearl fishers were so busy they did not <u>see</u> young Quinoro diving a <u>little way</u> from them. Quinoro <u>went</u> down to the sea-bed. He saw a <u>big</u> manta ray <u>go</u> by. A <u>group</u> of fish <u>swam quickly</u> among the sea-weeds. Quinoro <u>came up</u> with a <u>big</u> oyster in his hand.

When the fishermen <u>came home</u> and realized what had happened and that he was safe, they laughed about Quinoro's adventure. They were even more <u>happy</u> when he opened his oyster shell. There was a gleaming white pearl, the <u>biggest</u> they'd ever seen, and <u>worth a lot of money</u>! Quinoro was their hero!

enjoyed

certain

refused

lovely

begged

surfaced

wonderful

largest

huge

darted

massive

valuable

Find the partners

Some words tell you the gender of the person or animal it describes – whether it is male or female. For example:

(king and queen)

❑ Each of the shells below has lost its other half. Can you join up the pairs? Write the other partner in the matching half of the shell.

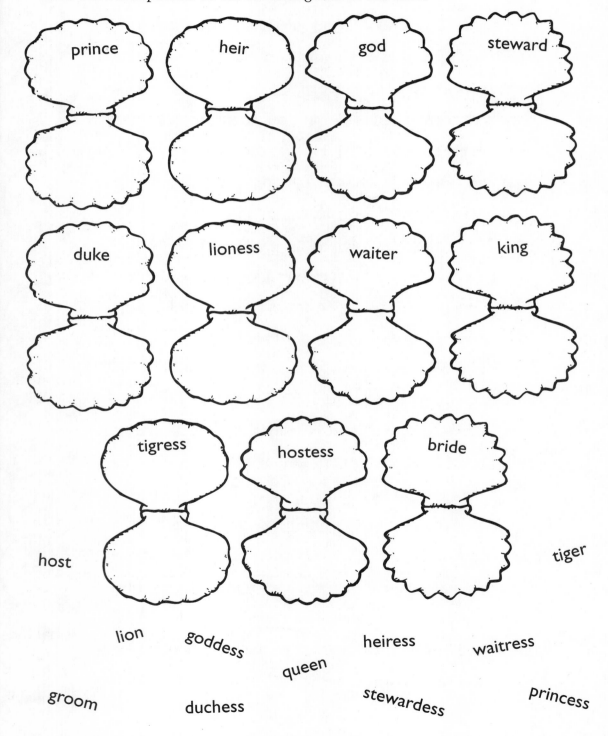

prince heir god steward

duke lioness waiter king

tigress hostess bride

host tiger

lion goddess heiress waitress

queen

groom duchess stewardess princess

Take your partners

❑ For each of the animals below there is a male and a female name. Choose the correct words to match the pictures from those listed at the side of the page and write them in the boxes, as in the first one. Use a dictionary to check the meanings.

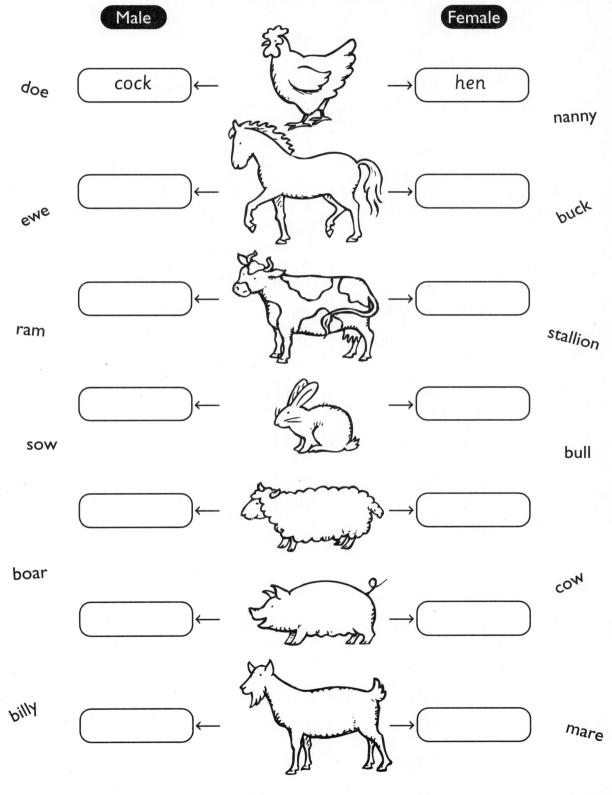

Male   Female

doe   cock ← → hen

            nanny

ewe   buck

ram   stallion

sow   bull

boar   cow

billy   mare

New for old

When Sam was helping his mum and dad clear out the attic, they found a diary that had been written by his great-great-granny. There were lots of old words in it that Sam didn't understand.

❑ Can you find out what these words mean? Write down their meanings, then draw pictures of them to help Sam discover about his great-great-granny's life.

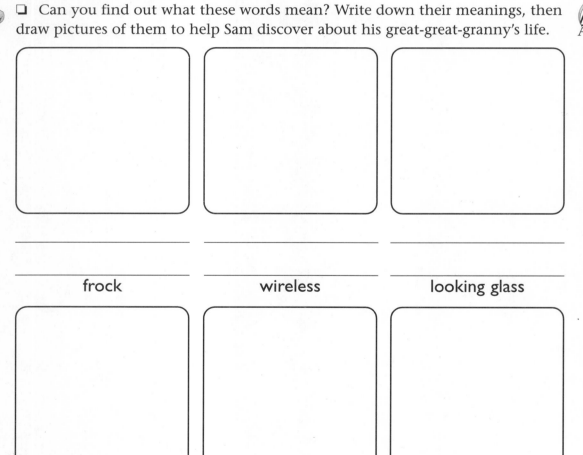

frock	wireless	looking glass
charabanc	perambulator	counterpane

Willing and able

All of the words below have the suffix **–able**:

washable

usable

agreeable

enjoyable   breakable

readable

reliable   pliable

❑ Can you find or work out what the suffix **–able** means?

_____

❑ Match each word from the above list to its correct definition:

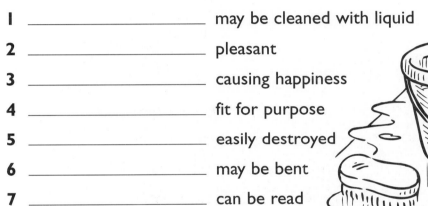

1 _____ may be cleaned with liquid

2 _____ pleasant

3 _____ causing happiness

4 _____ fit for purpose

5 _____ easily destroyed

6 _____ may be bent

7 _____ can be read

8 _____ trustworthy

If you are unsure of any words look them up in your dictionary.

❑ Now write each word in a sentence of your own.

1 _____

2 _____

3 _____

4 _____

5 _____

6 _____

7 _____

8 _____

Safe and sound

The suffix **–ible** means **able to be** (the same as the suffix –**able**).

❏ Write in your own words the meanings of the words below.
Write legibly!

1 legible _____

2 reversible _____

3 possible _____

4 incredible _____

5 invisible _____

6 responsible _____

7 sensible _____

8 flexible _____

9 visible _____

10 edible _____

❏ Check in your dictionary to see if you are right.

It is sens**ible** to be careful near the sea.

❏ Write a set of rules for safe bathing. One rule has been written for you.

Bathing code

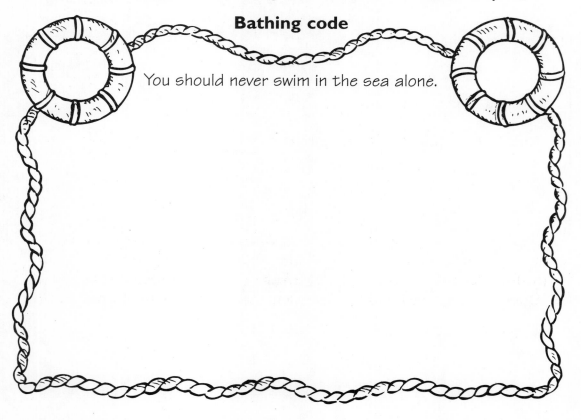

You should never swim in the sea alone.

Adding to adjectives

Adjectives are describing words. If you want to compare things, you can add the suffixes **–er** and **–est** to adjectives. For example:

Joe is tall Leon is tall**er** Nathan is tall**est**

❏ Choose the correct adjective for each illustration:

hottest

coldest

colder

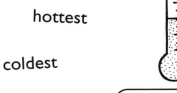 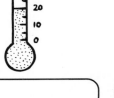 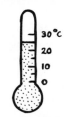 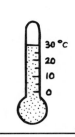

hungrier

hot

hungry

hotter

hungriest

cold

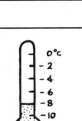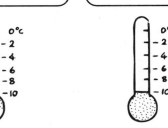

❏ Look at the words hungry, hungrier and hungriest again. What do you notice about how the spelling of the word changes when the suffix is added? Why does this happen with the word **hungry**, but not the word **cold**?

❏ Use what you have learned to complete these comparisons. Think carefully!

1 silly _____ _____

2 blue _____ _____

3 narrow _____ _____

Similar shells

❏ Answer the questions by colouring in the right shell.

Which is the hottest?   quite hot   hot   extremely hot

Which is the least cold?   quite cold   cold   very cold

Who is the happiest?   Sarah is happy.   Jasjeet is happier than Sarah.

Tom's watch is quite expensive. Gillian's watch is more expensive than Tom's, but Gregory's watch is the most expensive.
Who has the least expensive watch?

Tom   Gillian   Gregory

James is fairly sensible. Ryan is more sensible than James, but Stephen is the most sensible.
Who is extremely sensible?

James   Ryan   Stephen

Can you think of ways to compare your friends? For example, who is the most sporty?

❏ Make up your own sentences to compare them, using some of these words:

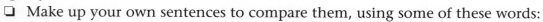
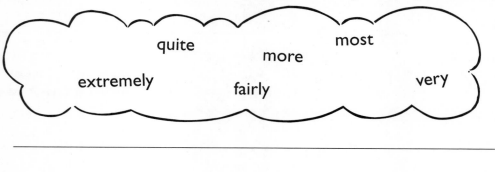

quite   most   more   extremely   fairly   very

_____

_____

_____

Find my mate!

Sometimes, two words can be joined together by using an apostrophe.
The new words that are formed are called contractions.

❏ Join together the words and their contractions.
The first one has been done for you.

❏ Now make a list of the pairs. The first one has been done for you.

Words in full	Contractions
does not	doesn't

❏ Write the contractions in your Word Explorer.
❏ Can you think of any more contractions? Write them below.

_____   _____

_____   _____

_____   _____

Long and short

When we speak we often join words together to make them shorter – we use contractions.

Cannot ⟶ can't	Do not ⟶ don't

Can't and **don't** are contractions. The **n't** part of the word is short for **not**.

❏ Write down what these words were before they were contracted. The first one has been done for you.

didn't ⟶ <u>did not</u>　　　hasn't ⟶ _____

hadn't ⟶ _____　　weren't ⟶ _____

doesn't ⟶ _____　　couldn't ⟶ _____

haven't ⟶ _____　　wasn't ⟶ _____

❏ Now look at the passage below. Replace the underlined words with their contractions.

My sister said I <u>cannot</u> go out to play this week because I <u>have not</u>

found the ball she gave me three weeks ago. I <u>did not</u> take it to

school and <u>it is</u> not in the house or up in the tree! My brother

says he <u>has not</u> got it but he <u>would not</u> tell me even if he had

taken it! I just <u>do not</u> know where it is but if I <u>have not</u> found it by

tonight <u>I will</u> get told off by my mum and dad and I might have to

go to bed early.

Underwater apostrophes (1)

Apostrophes can be used to show possession – to show that something belongs to something else. For example:

> The diver's flippers

The apostrophe shows that the flippers belong to the diver.

❑ Look at the illustrations below and for each one write down how the apostrophe is used for possession with these **singular** nouns. The first one has been done for you.

❑ Use your dictionary to help you spell the names of the sea creatures.

The sea dragon's

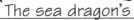
teeth

Underwater apostrophes (2)

In **the shark's fin**, the apostrophe shows that the fin belongs to the shark (singular).

But in **the sharks' fins**, the apostrophe shows that the fins belong to the sharks (plural).

Note that apostrophes do not always come before the **s**. To find out whether it should or not, you can turn the sentence around and use the word **of**. For example:

> The fin of the shark   The fins of the sharks

So, in the second example, the apostrophe should come at the end of the word.

❏ Look at the illustrations below. Put in the apostrophe in the correct place to show possession with these **plural** nouns.

❏ Use your dictionary to help you spell the names of the sea creatures.

The sea dragons' teeth

Columbus claims possession

In this passage, apostrophes have been used for contractions of words and to show possession.

❏ Underline contractions in red and possession words in blue:

Christopher Columbus's flagship was the Santa Maria. There were also two other ships on the journey of exploration, these were the Nina and the Pinta, but they weren't as big as the Santa Maria.

The Santa Maria's mainsail is famous for the large red cross, which you can see in the illustration. Its decks were made of wood and it had three masts. It was difficult for Columbus to gather a crew because of the fear people had of travelling into the unknown. They'd heard stories of sea monsters and mysterious whirlpools. Some even thought ships would fall off the edge of the world!

At the beginning of his exploration, Columbus didn't have much luck and the crew were afraid. It wasn't until they'd travelled for many months that land was sighted in the distance. A sailor's cry alerted them to it – they'd nearly reached land. The captain's excitement grew. He'd believed that by sailing west he would reach India, but instead they had landed on San Salvador's golden sands. In ignorance of this knowledge, Columbus claimed this New World as the possession of Spain.

Make the join

Connectives are words that can join one or more sentences to make a longer sentence. Read these four sentences:

> The rain fell heavily from the dark sky. The waves crashed against the side of the boat. The seagulls screeched overhead. The fishing trawler sailed on.

❏ Now look at how connectives can be used to make two instead of four sentences:

> The rain fell heavily from the dark sky **and** the waves crashed against the side of the boat. The seagulls screeched overhead, **but** the fishing trawler sailed on.

and and **but** are the connectives.

❏ Put these connectives in the right places to join the sentences. You can only use each connective once!

but   however   until   because   as   so

1 The huge crab scuttled over the shore _____ did not

stop at the rock pool _____ it wanted to return to its

home in the sea.

2 The red flag is flying _____ the lifeguard is not there;

_____ it may be possible to swim later on if the sea

becomes calm again.

3 People in deckchairs lazed on the beach _____ the

sun clouded over. Spots of rain started to fall _____

people dashed for cover.

What shall we do with the drunken sailor?

❏ Captain Stone, the pirate, has been drinking too much rum and he's having difficulty giving orders to his crew. Can you rearrange his words so that his orders make sense?

1 Get on your decks and scrub the knees!

_____
_____
_____
_____

2 When we next the reach treasure we'll bury our island.

_____
_____
_____
_____

3 Get the sweep and cabin my untidy! It is very broom

_____
_____
_____
_____

4 Get below and breakfast my cook!

_____
_____
_____
_____

5 The sinking has hit a ship! Help! We're rock

_____
_____
_____

❏ Explain the different meanings of these two sentences:

I drink what I like. _____

I like what I drink. _____

As good as gold

A simile compares one thing to another thing to create an image in the mind.
Similes usually begin with the words **as** or **like**.

❏ Draw the images created by these similes.

as brave as a lion	**as slow as a tortoise**
as fat as a pig	**as wise as an owl**

❏ Now complete these similes:

1 as bright as a _____	**6** as green as _____
2 as cold as _____	**7** as hard as _____
3 as cool as a _____	**8** as hot as _____
4 as flat as a _____	**9** as light as a _____
5 as fresh as a _____	**10** as quick as a _____

Treasure Test 1

❑ Can you spell these words on your empty Treasure Chest sheet? Ask a friend to test you on them. Remember! Look, say, cover, write, check. Write each word three times. Every time you get it right, colour in a pearl in the Treasure Chest shell.

above

across

afterwards

along

alright

also

around

before

below

behind

between

both

decide

different

difficult

digit

fall

fan

fasten

ferry

following

happen

high

hope

inside

interest

iron

island

❑ Write the ones you find tricky in your Word Explorer.

Treasure Test 2

❏ Can you spell these words on your empty Treasure Chest sheet? Ask a friend to test you on them. Remember! Look, say, cover, write, check. Write each word three times. Every time you get it right, colour in a pearl in the Treasure Chest shell.

near	only	open	other
outside	place	right	ring
round	such	sudden	though
through	together	tonight	under
where	which	without	why
yawn	year	yes	yet

❏ Write the ones you find tricky in your Word Explorer.

Words, words and more words

❏ All these words contain the letter **v**. Can you sort them according to whether they have **v** at the beginning or inside the word?

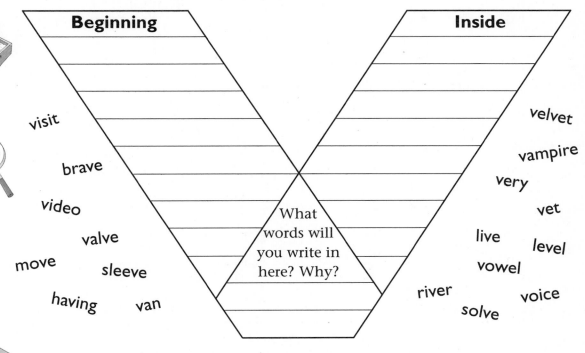

Beginning   Inside

visit
brave
video
valve
move   sleeve
having   van

What words will you write in here? Why?

velvet
vampire
very
vet
live   level
vowel
river   voice
solve

❏ Can you find any words in the dictionary that end with **v**?

In the two rows below, the letter **a** can be pronounced like **a** as in **day** or like **a** as in **hat**.

bake	Jake	rake	sake	take
back	Jack	rack	sack	tack

❏ How do you pronounce **a** in the top row? As in **day** or as in **hat**? _____

How do you pronounce **a** in the bottom row? _____

❏ Write down a spelling rule about how –**ck** and –**ke** change the sound of the vowel:

_____

_____

_____

❏ Add **or** to complete these words:

w_____d,   w_____k,   w_____ld,   w_____m,   w_____st,   w_____ship

❏ How is –**or** pronounced in these words?

Write the phoneme that normally makes this sound. _____

Walrus words

❏ Add **wo** or **wa** to these letters to make a proper word:

1 _____rk	**4** _____lf	**7** _____ter	**10** _____rld
2 _____man	**5** _____lrus	**8** _____rn	**11** _____rship
3 _____ll	**6** _____nder	**9** _____rd	**12** _____n

❏ Write each new word in your own sentence.

1 _____

_____

2 _____

_____

3 _____

_____

4 _____

_____

5 _____

_____

6 _____

_____

7 _____

_____

8 _____

9 _____

10 _____

11 _____

12 _____

A walrus wallows
near the water.

Sound it out!

Some words contain the same group of letters, but the words sound different from each other when you say them. Say these words carefully:

tough	thought	plough

❏ Now sort these words into their correct sound groups:

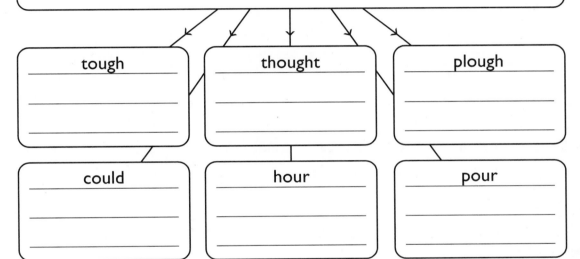

enough	flour	would	bought
slough	should	fought	bough
four	sour	tour	rough

tough	thought	plough
____	____	____
____	____	____

could	hour	pour
____	____	____
____	____	____

❏ Find other words in your dictionary that have the same group of letters as these:

br**ight** _____ _____ _____

ju**dge** _____ _____ _____

Porthole problems

❑ The words missing from the sentences can be found in the portholes. Choose the most suitable word for each sentence, write it in the space and shade the prefix used in it.

1 Captain Stone _____ the rusty padlock on the treasure chest, but the pirates were _____ when they found that it was full of pebbles.

2 The sinking ship was _____ below the surface so we made a swift _____ onto the life boats.

3 I read in a _____ book that British goods were _____ on ships to countries all over the world.

4 The crew managed to _____ the secret message on the treasure map but we _____ on which island to set sail for.

5 The strong winds out at sea _____ the ship from setting sail so it _____ the harbour.

6 Pirates often died from slight injuries because _____ and _____ had not been discovered during their lifetimes.

7 It was our _____ that the navigator made a _____ and the ship sailed straight onto rocks.

8 The number of the crew was _____ when five men were left marooned on an island.

9 Captain Stone and his crew were _____ by a naval ship, after they had escaped in a long boat.

10 "If everyone _____ and listens to me, we'll find the treasure!" shouted Captain Stone.

Portholes (left column): exit, mistake, unhappy, antibiotics, exported, disagreed, re-entered, prevented

Portholes (right column): decode, decreased, antiseptics, non-fiction, unlocked, misfortune, co-operates, disappearing, recaptured

What a catch!

❑ Underline the suffixes in the fishy words. Write the words in the correct net:

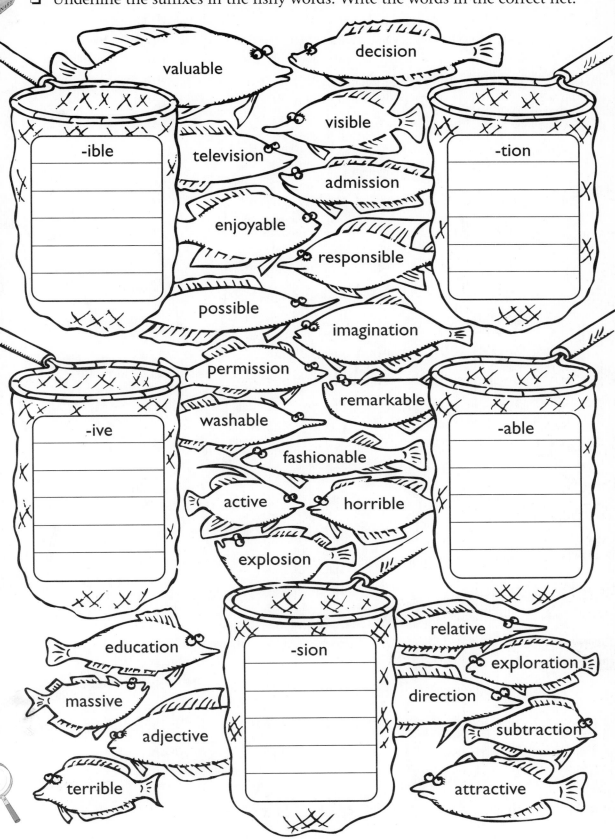

valuable

decision

-ible

visible

-tion

television

admission

enjoyable

responsible

possible

imagination

permission

-ive

washable

remarkable

-able

fashionable

active

horrible

explosion

relative

education

-sion

exploration

massive

direction

adjective

subtraction

terrible

attractive

Captain Stone's tattoos

The tattooed root words on the back of Captain Stone's hand need to join with one of the suffixes on his fingers and thumb to make new words.

❏ The root words on the scars need changing first and then adding to the correct finger. Think carefully about whether you can simply add the suffix on to the root word, or whether you need to make any other changes!

Three examples have been done for you already. Use a dictionary to check your new words.

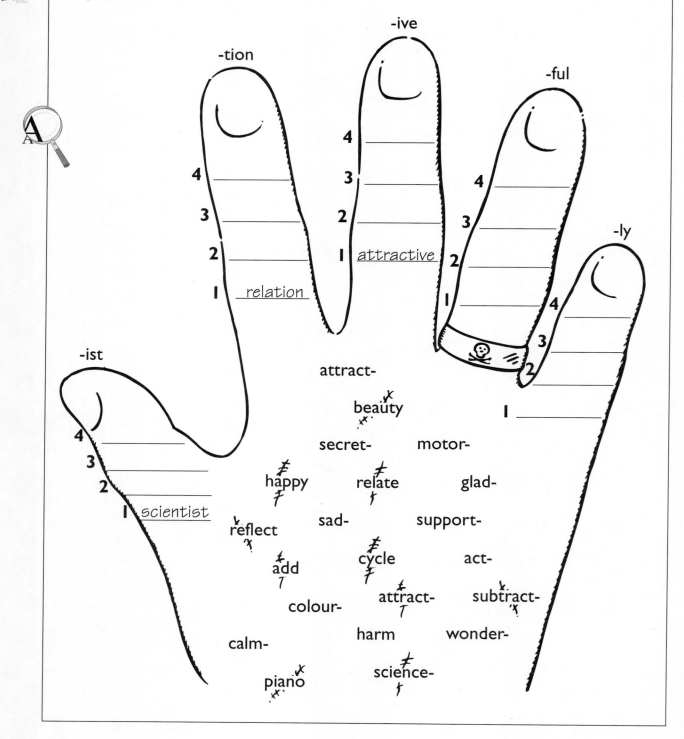

It's and Its

Its without an apostrophe shows possession (belonging to). For example:

The bird flapped its wings.

It's with an apostrophe shows a contraction (missing letter **i**). For example:

It's a girl!

❏ Underline the correct usage in the panels in each of these sentences:

1 The cow swished [it's / <u>its</u>] tail.

2 [It's / Its] raining fast now.

3 [It's / Its] broken!

4 Where is [it's / its] cover?

5 [It's / Its] fur was soaked.

6 [It's / Its] nearly time for the bell.

7 The toy had lost [it's / its] battery.

8 The kitten licked [it's / its] paw.

9 The bicycle lost [it's / its] wheel.

10 My mum always tells me [it's / its] important to hand in my homework on time.

11 Perhaps [it's / its] true what she told us.

12 I can't understand how [it's / its] possible.

Gone fishing

A compound word is when two separate words join to make one word.

❏ Catch the correct fish to make a new word. Write the new word next to the fishing line. The first one has been done for you.

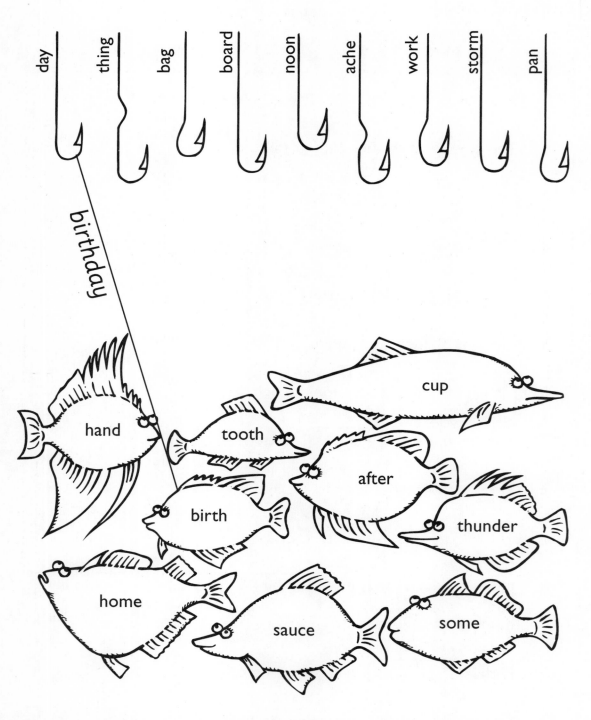

birthday

Hooks: day, thing, bag, board, noon, ache, work, storm, pan

Fish: hand, cup, tooth, after, birth, thunder, home, sauce, some

❏ Now think of some other compound words and write them in your word explorer after you have checked them in your dictionary.

Animal diminutives

A **diminutive** is a word that refers to smallness. For example:

    the diminutive of **dog** is **puppy**.

❏ Map these nouns to their diminutives.
One has been completed for you.

Noun	Diminutive
dog	foal
cow	gosling
cat	tadpole
horse	cygnet
hare	cub
frog	kitten
eel	elver
swan	leveret
goose	puppy
fox	lamb
lion	calf
sheep	cub

More diminutives

The word diminutive refers to smallness.

❏ Complete these sentences, using a dictionary to help you.

A booklet is a small _____

A maisonette is a small _____

A duckling is a small _____

An owlet is a small _____

A hillock is a small _____

A piglet is a small _____

A gosling is a small _____

A kitchenette is a small _____

A sapling is a small _____

❏ Which suffixes have been used in the diminutives?

–let _____   – _____   – _____   – _____

❏ Which two diminutives are very different to their root words?   _____   _____

❏ Which of these two words comes from the French language and what does it mean?

_____

_____

_____

Argue the point!

Connectives are joining words and are often used in an argument:

> It is important to keep rivers, seas and oceans clean <u>because</u> pollution can harm animals and people.

❏ Put the right connective in the spaces below:

so unless if because then

1 Do not swim in the sea _____ there is a lifeguard on the beach.

2 Always wear a life-jacket when you go out on a boat _____ you might fall in the water.

3 You should always wear sunscreen _____ you are going to play on the beach on a hot, sunny day.

4 There are sometimes broken bottles and other discarded rubbish on the beach _____ it is important to wear something on your feet.

5 If you have been stung by a jellyfish _____ you must go to the hospital.

❏ Make up your own arguments using these connectives:

1 unless _____

_____

2 if _____

_____

3 because _____

_____

4 so _____

_____

Can you ask a question?

It is possible to make a statement into a question by changing the order of the words in the statement and adding a question mark.

It is very stormy at sea today. ➔ <u>Is it</u> very stormy at sea today?

❑ Can you make these statements into questions?

There are many exciting creatures that live in the sea.

_____

It is necessary to wear a life-jacket when you go sailing.

_____

You can often find crabs in rock pools on the beach.

_____

It is fun to make sandcastles on the sea-shore.

_____

❑ Write a statement about each picture and then make the statements into questions:

Statement

_____

Question

_____

Statement

_____

Question

_____

Statement

_____

Question

_____

Test your tenses!

❏ Write the past tense of these regular verbs by adding **ed**.

For example: I talk → I talk**ed**

I show→_____	I wait→_____	I look→_____
I want→_____	I pick→_____	I touch→_____
I wish→_____	I play→_____	I ask→_____

Which suffix did you add? (_____)

❏ Write the past tense of these regular verbs by adding the suffix **ed**.

For example: I cry → I cr**ied**   I tap → I tap**ped**

List (a)

I try → _____

I spy → _____

I marry → _____

I hurry → _____

I bury → _____

List (b)

I hum → _____

I pat → _____

I beg → _____

I trip → _____

I trot → _____

❏ What rules did you discover for lists (a) and (b)?

(a) _____

(b) _____

❏ Change these sentences, which are in the present tense, into the future tense:

1 I sit at my desk. → <u>I will sit at my desk.</u>

2 John travels home by bus. → _____
_____

3 They love their presents. → _____
_____

4 She places the books on the shelf. → _____
_____

5 Mum drives to work. → _____
_____

Treasures of the sea

A tense tells us when something is happening. A tense can be past, present or future.

The passage below is written in the present tense because it is happening now.

I am searching.

❏ Change the words that are underlined in to the past tense, to show that things have already happened.

I was searching.

Write the new words in the boxes. Illustrate your work when you have finished.

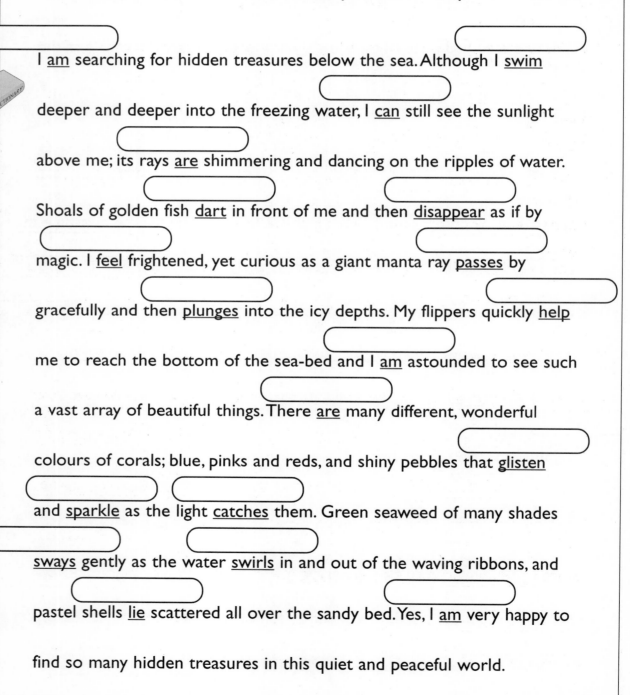

I <u>am</u> searching for hidden treasures below the sea. Although I <u>swim</u>

deeper and deeper into the freezing water, I <u>can</u> still see the sunlight

above me; its rays <u>are</u> shimmering and dancing on the ripples of water.

Shoals of golden fish <u>dart</u> in front of me and then <u>disappear</u> as if by

magic. I <u>feel</u> frightened, yet curious as a giant manta ray <u>passes</u> by

gracefully and then <u>plunges</u> into the icy depths. My flippers quickly <u>help</u>

me to reach the bottom of the sea-bed and I <u>am</u> astounded to see such

a vast array of beautiful things. There <u>are</u> many different, wonderful

colours of corals; blue, pinks and reds, and shiny pebbles that <u>glisten</u>

and <u>sparkle</u> as the light <u>catches</u> them. Green seaweed of many shades

<u>sways</u> gently as the water <u>swirls</u> in and out of the waving ribbons, and

pastel shells <u>lie</u> scattered all over the sandy bed. Yes, I <u>am</u> very happy to

find so many hidden treasures in this quiet and peaceful world.

Danger at sea!

The passage below is written in the past tense. It tells us that something has already happened.

The boat sailed across the ocean.

❏ Change the passage in to the present tense, as if it is happening now.

The boat sails across the ocean.

The lines tell you where you will need to alter the passage.

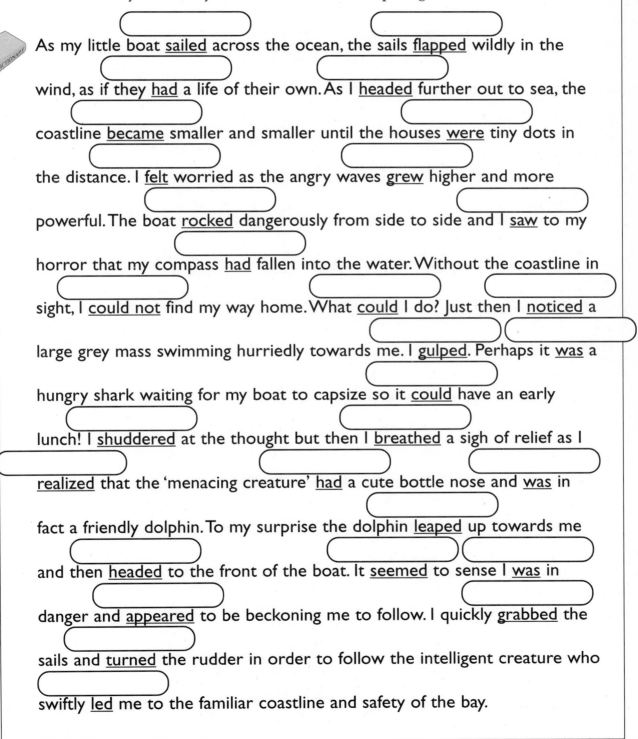

As my little boat <u>sailed</u> across the ocean, the sails <u>flapped</u> wildly in the

wind, as if they <u>had</u> a life of their own. As I <u>headed</u> further out to sea, the

coastline <u>became</u> smaller and smaller until the houses <u>were</u> tiny dots in

the distance. I <u>felt</u> worried as the angry waves <u>grew</u> higher and more

powerful. The boat <u>rocked</u> dangerously from side to side and I <u>saw</u> to my

horror that my compass <u>had</u> fallen into the water. Without the coastline in

sight, I <u>could not</u> find my way home. What <u>could</u> I do? Just then I <u>noticed</u> a

large grey mass swimming hurriedly towards me. I <u>gulped</u>. Perhaps it <u>was</u> a

hungry shark waiting for my boat to capsize so it <u>could</u> have an early

lunch! I <u>shuddered</u> at the thought but then I <u>breathed</u> a sigh of relief as I

<u>realized</u> that the 'menacing creature' <u>had</u> a cute bottle nose and <u>was</u> in

fact a friendly dolphin. To my surprise the dolphin <u>leaped</u> up towards me

and then <u>headed</u> to the front of the boat. It <u>seemed</u> to sense I <u>was</u> in

danger and <u>appeared</u> to be beckoning me to follow. I quickly <u>grabbed</u> the

sails and <u>turned</u> the rudder in order to follow the intelligent creature who

swiftly <u>led</u> me to the familiar coastline and safety of the bay.

Getting it right

> Our planet, Earth, is part and part sea.

A word has been omitted from this sentence so that it doesn't make sense.
We correct it using an omission symbol, like this:

> land
> Our planet, Earth, is part ^ and part sea.

❏ Correct these sentences using the omission symbol:

1 There is more than land.
          ^

2 The largest seas called oceans.
                 ^

3 Oceans are as deep mountains are high.

4 The Atlantic Ocean about five thousand kilometres across.

5 Some of the first Atlantic explorers the Vikings.

6 They crossed the ocean discovered America.

7 This was five hundred before Columbus set out.

8 Vikings travelled in long which had large sails.

9 On the of the ship was a carving of a dragon's head.

10 If there was no wind were used to propel the long ship.

How well can you spell?

❑ Read this story carefully and correct any spelling mistakes that you spot by crossing them out and placing the correct spellings above them.
Use a dictionary to check your spellings.

When I was yung I decided that I wanted to be a sailor like my

older bother. My muver and farther didunt want me to leve home,

but evry day I thort about how exciting life at sea would be.

On my sixteenth brithday, early in the mornin I opend my

bedroom window and jumpt out. I had a chanje of clothes and

some muney with me. I new that I mite nevver see my family again

as I walkt towards the coast.

I fownd work on a ship carrying goods a cross the Atlantic

Ocean, but befor sailing I begane to thinck about my parents having

to do my werk as well as their oan. The ship was about to leve but I

thort it would be betta for me to return home. For the secund

time in my life I ran away, but this time I was doing the rite thing.

When I returned to the plaice where I belonged, my wite-haired

mother tolled me how happie she was that I had returned.

I stoped on the farm and togeather we made mutch money.

Treasure chest